Joe Jusko's Art of Edgar Rice Burroughs

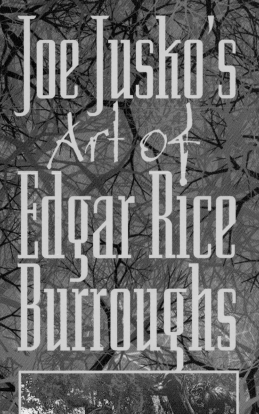

MW00852460

Dedication

To Frank Frazetta, whose
praise and encouragement
for these works will inspire me
for countless years to come.
And to Michael Friedlander,
who had more faith in me than
I had in myself.

FPG

Acknowledgements

The publishers are sincerely grateful
for the hard work and dedication of
Danton Burroughs, Sandra Galfis,
Will Hagenlocher and Rick Ulaky.

Book design by Kirby Kiser
Edited by John Zaphyr

Copyright ©1994-1996, Edgar Rice
Burroughs, Inc. All rights reserved.

Trademarks, TARZAN®, BARSOOM™ and
JOHN CARTER, WARLORD OF MARS™
are owned by Edgar Rice Burroughs, Inc.
and used by permission.

No part of this book may be reproduced or
transmitted in any form or by any means,
electronic or mechanical, including
photocopying, recording, or any information
storage and retrieval system, without
written permission from the publisher.

Library of Congress Catalog Card Number:
96-084505

ISBN# 1-887569-14-6

First printing: July 1996

Published by FPG
2539 Washington Road
Building 1000
Pittsburgh, PA 15241

Printed in Hong Kong

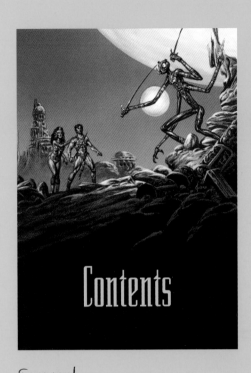

Contents

Foreword

by Michael Friedlander

When we originally approached Joe Jusko with the idea of creating one hundred and twenty new paintings based on Edgar Rice Burroughs' famous stories, I had no idea that we were getting involved in the making of what I consider to be the greatest single collection of Burroughs art to date.

Ever since I can remember, *fantasy and science fiction* has been a huge part of my life. From a young age, I would get lost in the fantastic worlds of Robert E. Howard, Michael Moorcock, and of course, Edgar Rice Burroughs. I was a big comic book fan growing up as well and, in particular, would buy all titles relating to sword & sorcery. And that's where I first became familiar with Joe Jusko's work. I purchased every issue of Marvel Comic's *Savage Sword of Conan* magazine and it's there around 1981, that I started seeing these powerful covers by Joe. I didn't know who he was at the time, but I absolutely loved his work. If Conan were alive and well, I imagine he would look like he does in Joe's paintings.

Now moving up to 1992, I again ran across Joe's work. This time, in a large collection done for the first *Marvel Masterpieces* trading card series. We were also producing trading cards at that time and, in fact, negotiating for the rights to produce Burroughs cards. Once we obtained the rights to do them, I knew that the guy I wanted to work on an entirely new Burroughs project was Joe Jusko. I was confident that he could capture the power, drama and excitement of Burroughs' creations. And he did not let me down. His renditions are among the best I have seen.

I remember a conversation that took place between Joe and I concerning the backs of the trading cards for his first series. When I told him that we were going to reproduce the best Burroughs paintings by the likes of Neal Adams, Frank Frazetta, Roy Krenkel, J. Allen St. John and Boris Vallejo on the backs, he nearly had a heart attack. I explained that we wanted to compile this spectacular collection of Burroughs art and this would be a great way to present it. It was only natural for him to be intimidated by this proposal but I saw the quality of work he was producing and was confident that it was equal to that of his peers. So we printed Joe's new paintings on the fronts and the best of the classic Burroughs art on the backs, and in my opinion, it was a very successful combination; one that allows the enthusiast to appreciate both the old and the new interpretations of Burroughs' wonderful creations.

I hope you will agree that Joe's paintings do indeed capture all the magic and excitement that is contained in Edgar Rice Burroughs' imaginative novels. Rarely does one get the chance to see such a striking combination of art and story come together as it does here. Unquestionably, this is the world of Edgar Rice Burroughs and the art of Joe Jusko at their very best!

Introduction: Joe Jusko: Edgar Rice Burroughs Artist for the 90's

by Danton Burroughs

The works of Edgar Rice Burroughs have provided a rich resource for artists to display their collective talents. What Burroughs conceived in his many novels, a wide variety of artists have visualized with pen, ink and brush. Over the decades, certain artists have done work which has stood out to become the defining images of books for that era. J.Allen St. John comes most quickly to mind as being the first of these artists. In the years since, others have emerged to define the works of ERB for their time. Frank Frazetta did the most popular covers for Burroughs books in the 1960's and '70's. Michael Whelan's eleven Mars covers remain his only Burroughs illustrations, but he captured the ambiance of romantic adventure just as surely as the best artists of the 1920's and 1930's could ever have hoped.

In the 1990's, another new talent has emerged to bring his own insights to bear on the massive literary output of Edgar Rice Burroughs. That artist is Joe Jusko. No other single artist has ever done 125 paintings based on ERB before and, in so doing, he has carefully represented all of ERB's works, adding some very memorable and colorful images to the artistic lexicon generated by these many stories.

Tarzan is certainly one of the prominent images in this series, representing nearly half of Joe's paintings. Every artist brings an individual feel to the jungle ambiance of Tarzan and, with Joe, we see a variety of approaches which emphasize a slick dynamism that proves these novels, some written 80 years ago, can still capture the imagination of the modern reader.

In a scene from **The Beasts of Tarzan** which Joe has titled *Hunting Party* (page 25), Tarzan stands out in almost three-dimensional contrast to the subdued dark green background of the jungle and the blue-black of the beasts around him. Another almost 3-D effect is achieved in *Landslide* (page 41), a scene from **Tarzan and the Lost Empire.**

However, Joe approaches each scene differently, and the artist is clearly taken with the many opportunities for dramatic illustration provided by the first Tarzan book. In the painting named *Bolgani Attack* (page 17), the primitive menace of the jungle is depicted by showing the adolescent Tarzan confronted by Bolgani the gorilla, while emphasizing the size differential between the two figures.

La of Opar (page 21) has long been a favorite of both artists and fans, and Joe's rendering of this mythic figure captures her exotic, erotic and menacing aspects, all in one.

Joe also renders atmospheric scenes, as well as those of tense excitement. In the image from **Tarzan the Magnificent** titled *Ancient Explorer* (page 58), he portrays the seldom illustrated scene in which Tarzan discovers the bleached bones of a lost traveler. And, while other artists tend to overlook **Tarzan and the Forbidden City**, Joe creates one of his most dynamic paintings in which the ape man attacks a dinosaur in a scene aptly titled *Jurassic Battle* (page 56).

Many of Joe's illustrations are striking enough to be book covers. *Airborne* (page 27), from **The Son of Tarzan**, is only one of many examples.

In one particular scene taken from a Tarzan book, the ape man doesn't appear at all. Yet, one doesn't even think about his absence, since Joe's rendering of *Balza, the Wild Girl* (page 50) is so intensely erotic. Burroughs, himself, would probably have been amused to see someone do a painting of what he expected readers would only be allowed to visualize. While probably too risque' an image for a book cover, it certainly would sell a lot of books!

In his portrayal of *The Gryf* (page 34), the colorful background Joe puts in this scene sets the exciting foreground image off nicely. Color is used to create a very different effect in *Spectre* (page 37), in which the fire in the foreground truly illuminates the darkness in a scene from **Tarzan and the Golden Lion**. It is this variety of approaches and effects in Joe's paintings that stamp them with originality, making Joe's efforts stand on their own despite the many hundreds of images based on the Burroughs collection done by other artists in decades past.

Joe is especially effective in the scenes he shows taking place underwater. In *Fatal Plunge* (page 46), from **Tarzan the Triumphant**, the water filling the frame is rendered in different shades of blue and is off-set by the white bubbles and impact point at the top of the painting, all of which emphasize the peril of the prisoner in the net. Joe employs the color blue to a very different effect in *Stranded* (page 20), a scene from **The Return of Tarzan**. This painting captures, in one frozen moment, the awesome sense of beauty and remoteness that Tarzan finds so wondrous about the realm that was Africa at the turn of the century. Joe portrays the ocean as a place both of spectacle and menace, such as one can only experience in a place far from the tracks of civilization.

But, as much attention as Joe brings to bear on Tarzan, he gives equal interest to the non-Tarzan books, such as the adventures set in the Earth's Core, on Mars and on Venus.

Prehistoric Encounter (page 106) is a spectacular panorama of Pellucidar which perfectly captures what each and every Earth's Core novel is about. In this painting, there is a beautiful, nearly naked cave girl, prehistoric animals on the verge of battle and a fiery volcano in the distance. This is how adventure should look! Another day in the life of Pellucidar is captured in *Outnumbered* (page 99), in which a vicious saber-toothed tiger is attacked by three Thipdars. The scattered human bones on the ground demonstrate that life and death struggles are clearly constant in Pellucidar.

In *Tentacled Terror* (page 105), Joe portrays a dramatic encounter with a seldom seen, tentacled monster of Pellucidar, as described in **Land of Terror**. This is another scene which is worthy of a cover and entices you to read the book, based on just

this single image.

Joe doesn't overlook **The Land That Time Forgot** either. His painting, titled *Plesiosaur* (page 120), captures the essence of that book so perfectly, and with such a colorful and arresting image, that a new printing of the book should be rushed-out with this piece as the cover to attract new fans immediately! Joe also captured the Lost World ambience of the Caspack series beautifully in his painting titled *Tyrannosaur* (page 119), which also captures a sense of old Hollywood film classics in its execution.

It's interesting to note the different approaches Joe uses with color. The science-fiction books of ERB are cause for Joe to indulge in wild and colorful otherworldly vistas that can not help but fire the imagination upon viewing them. There are many such examples, one of which is *Quick Draw* (page 125) from **Beyond the Farthest Star**. This was one of my grandfather's last stories, but it showed that the yen to explore strange new worlds was still very much a part of his creative being.

An image one could only see in the card series by assembling six chase cards is a vista featuring John Carter and Dejah Thoris surrounded by some of the imaginative denizens of Mars: a white ape, two green Martians, three plant men and a Banth. This wonderful panorama called *Under the Moons of Mars* (page 62) also includes three Martian flyers above an ancient city in the background, while the two moons of Mars shine down over all. It truly speaks to the atmosphere of ERB's novels of Barsoom.

The chase cards of Series Two similarly captured the rarefied atmosphere of Mars, yet more erotically in a scene of Thuvia (who has never looked more alluring in all her 80 years of fictional life), off-set by two dangerous looking Banths. *Thuvia, Maid of Mars* (page 77) is an inspired piece of work, and another which demands to grace the cover of a book.

Joe has chosen to render the green Martians as being thinner than previous artists have generally done. This approach tends to give them an unusual spidery quality, and actually serves to make them appear even more alien.

Barsoom is a rich source of inspiration for Joe's brush, as his many Martian paintings all explore this imaginative alien vista in different and exciting ways. *Eyes in the Dark* (page 70) is a dramatic concept in which glowing red eyes prey on our imagination. But *Barricade* (page 86) is surely one of the most arresting images in the series. The startling scene where the three gigantic arms of an otherwise unseen white ape struggles to grab Hadron of Hastor in their deadly embrace, genuinely captures the wonder and adventure of **A Fighting Man of Mars**, one of the best of the Martian series.

For some reason, the children of the green Martians have rarely been rendered by artists. However, in *Baby Thark* (page 67), Joe depicts just how truly ugly these critters can be, even as they crack open their shells! Certainly, an inspired image. Just as inspired is *Face of Death* (page 66), a very extreme close-up of an angry adult Thark.

Then, Joe takes us in a very different direction with *Lair of the Assassins* (page 89), a vista which is both colorful and moody, also giving us a glimpse of Martian statuary and architecture. This one is detailed enough to be a poster.

Not to be outdone, even by himself, Joe continues to surpass previous paintings in his series by coming up with different and unexpected images. The painting he calls *Chamber of Reptiles* (page 74), in which John Carter and Woola face a room of weird, reptilian aliens, is rendered in green tones which serve to emphasize the all-out strangeness of this scene.

The White Death [(page 87) another stunner from **A Fighting Man of Mars**] is an oft-illustrated scene, but Joe's version is dramatic and exciting nonetheless. Some scenes in the novels are just too good to ignore.

I can't remember the last time I saw an artist do a painting of an Apt from **The Warlords of Mars**, but Joe goes full tilt to make *Apt Encounter* (page 73) one of the most exciting visuals in his series. But Joe also demonstrates that even the *Aftermath* (page 76) of a battle can be rich in atmosphere and detail. This is another sure candidate for a poster.

The Ulsio is another, seldom seen critter and, in *Strangling the Ulsio* (page 82), we see why it is considered a repulsive creature by all the races of Barsoom.

Not since Roy Krenkel and Frank Frazetta did such evocative covers for the Ace Venus series in the 1960's, has any artist tackled these stories with the enthusiasm demonstrated by Joe Jusko. The two paintings *Sea Beasts* (page 116) and *The Boiling Sea* (page 115) form a pair of related images of Venusian sea monsters locked in combat. One painting emphasizes the creatures themselves, while the other is a wider seascape showing the cloudy Venusian sky where the sunlight sometimes pokes through to boil the sea below. The color in these two paintings is really stunning and marks them as some of the best in the series. Joe also clearly likes the color of the Tharban, a red and white Venusian beast which he dramatically depicts in three different paintings.

Some artists of the ERB paperbacks in recent years have inadvisedly attempted to modernize the look of the covers. However, Joe Jusko, in the tradition of the best artists that proceeded him, has adapted his artistic style to the requirements of illustrating in the romantic tradition represented by the type of fiction Burroughs wrote. While these may be old-fashioned adventures, the stories are still fresh and exciting. This feeling of excitement is what Joe Jusko's art communicates.

Edgar Rice Burroughs wrote in a tradition which was popular in the first half of the 20th century. But, while the tastes of the reading public have changed in regard to much of the fiction it reads today, compared to what was being read fifty years ago, the novels of Edgar Rice Burroughs endure, are loved, discovered and rediscovered with all the affection of the timeless tales of Sherlock Holmes by Sir Arthur Conan Doyle. Some dreams never die but remain rich and vital, generation after generation. This is what Edgar Rice Burroughs achieved and this is the vitality Joe Jusko has succeeded in capturing in his mammoth tribute to the imagination of ERB. The stories of Edgar Rice Burroughs are very much alive in these paintings by Joe Jusko.

UNDER THE MOONS OF MARS

(detail)

Painting Burroughs

by Joe Jusko

My involvement with the worlds of Edgar Rice Burroughs began when Michael Friedlander approached me about doing a painted card series for FPG. Our original premise was going to be an all encompassing "Joe Jusko's Babes and Barbarians" project. A few months later, as I was finishing the card set I had been working on, Mike called me again, to see if I'd be interested in painting an entire card series based on the novels of Burroughs. Being a fan of my Conan work, he thought that I would be well suited for the Burroughs project. Truthfully, I never thought I would be offered the Burroughs property and I was excited to have the chance to do it. Burroughs' work covers everything that I like to paint, so naturally I jumped at the chance to take the job.

The works of Burroughs were in tune with my strengths. Drawing active figures, big cats, natural backgrounds, those are all more intriguing to me than drawing dragons, wizards and other mythological creatures. Furthermore, I have always been a fan of the Burroughs novels and related comics. People my age grew up with the Neal Adams, Frank Frazetta and Boris Vallejo covers which attracted us in the first place to Burroughs' work. When I was younger, I found them to be not only intriguing but very exciting.

Perhaps the biggest difficulty in starting this project was narrowing my choices down to one scene per card. This may not seem to be a problem but in actuality it was a huge hurdle. Rick Ulaky, an extremely devoted Burroughs fan, proved to be an invaluable help by reading the books and writing "Cliff Notes" for me. He would block out character descriptions, scene synopses, and detail where certain scenes were located in the books. Sometimes, we would have twenty-five scenes in a single book to choose from. Unfortunately, when you're dealing with the sheer volume of books that Burroughs wrote, you may only have room for two or three scenes from each book. It came down to picking the scenes I knew I could get right the first time.

I took the novels Michael and Rick had sent me, and I reread chapters that contained scenes I thought would make good card images. I would reread, not only that scene, but the entire chapter around that scene. A lot of times, Burroughs would leave certain parts of character descriptions out, such as hair color and clothing, leaving me pretty much to my own discretion. To prepare, I read and researched as much as possible. **The Burroughs Bestiary** became my "Bible," since it contained different descriptions of Burroughs' characters and lands. I purchased an entire run of ERBdoms before I started the card series, reading those from start to finish. Since I'm not an authority on Burroughs, I found articles by writers such as John Flint Roy and Larry Ivie to be very helpful in giving me more details and patterns to go by.

Of course, time was a factor in successfully completing this card series. I decided to work with an image area of 8.25"x11.25". This afforded me enough space to get in the required detail for each scene while keeping the paintings small enough to complete in a timely fashion. Being an extremely impatient painter, working in acrylics was also instrumental in completing the series in an expeditious manner, as they dry almost immediately. For the Burroughs card series, the average time for me was probably two days per painting, in succession. This schedule became fairly grueling after a while, making it difficult to keep my mind sharp while being original with every piece. Many times, I couldn't even pause to think or do more research. And, worse yet, there was no time to repaint a piece if I thought I had gotten it wrong. Those familiar with the paintings in card form will no doubt notice I have made some changes for this book: the absence of navels from the Barsoomian populace, and the addition of Nkima's tail in *Landslide* (which was mysteriously amputated somewhere between the pencil stage and the finished painting). In hindsight, these errors stand out, but are sometimes overlooked in the midst of such a laborious undertaking.

All in all, the Burroughs project was a rewarding experience. The fun part about doing Burroughs was

the diversity of his works. For instance, when I was doing the Tarzan pieces, I was totally into Tarzan. I had tunnel vision. But, when I painted other characters and scenes, I had to broaden my thinking, imagining how other characters would view these worlds. My approach in doing the cards was to do one series at a time rather than bouncing back and forth. This way, I wouldn't lose my perspective on each series. And I had forgotten how much I actually enjoyed the Mars books until I reread them preparing for this card series. As I started illustrating, I developed a real fondness for them again, recalling the rich detail and imagination they contain.

Another aspect of the card series that I found rewarding was being able to paint Burroughs' characters other than the main heroes, such as Tarzan, John Carter, Carson Napier and David Innes. Obviously, when painting book covers the focus has to be on the main character. However, I viewed this card series as being a whole compilation of scenes. Everybody knew this was an Edgar Rice Burroughs project, so the main characters didn't have to appear on every card. I was free to do scenes such as Lady Barbara Collis being pulled into the water in **Tarzan Triumphant** or a jungle warrior from **Tarzan and the City of Gold** being chased by lions. Even though these scenes didn't include main characters, they made excellent visuals. When I went through the Tarzan books as an illustrator, I tried to find scenes that were not typical. I did a few of the "key" scenes other artists had done before but I mostly chose scenes that have never been painted. I wanted to bring a new light to the Burroughs collection.

Most importantly, I wanted to be original. However, maintaining that sense of originality throughout a long series can be difficult. Sometimes all the cards in a series have a tendency to blend together, losing their individual personalities. To prevent this from happening, I tried to avoid certain elements. One involved the color schemes. A problem that sometimes can arise from doing that many paintings, so quickly, is to fall into a pattern of using color schemes you know will work, relying on them to finish the piece so you can move on to the next one. How many blue skies can you paint before they all start to look the same? The Tarzan scenes, as a rule, take place in the jungle, so I tried to vary the colors in the foliage as much as possible. I used colors other than green, maybe a combination of green with a

different color, and I would use various colors for reflected light, just to break the schemes up a bit. In certain pieces, I took a lot of color chances and found out that spontaneity often worked to my advantage.

The other problem that hampers originality is the development of a repetitive nature to the compositions. What can happen is you begin to use four or five of your favorite pose schemes over and over again. In trying to avoid this trap, I challenged myself to paint each scene from a different perspective or vantage point. You'll notice a lot of the cards have shots of Tarzan's head or back. When you're painting one hundred and twenty pieces over all, every one doesn't have to include his face. It sometimes works in doing composition if the character's face can't be seen. In fact, in a lot of instances, the character's face takes away from what's important in the painting.

How to portray Tarzan also was a challenge. As you might have noticed, I did not paint a "traditional" Tarzan. I consciously beefed him up, making him look more formidable. I don't think this is such a departure from what Burroughs wanted. There are many instances where Burroughs mentions Tarzan's muscular form. And I don't think that changing Tarzan physically was a disturbance to Burroughs' work, as much as it was an effort to keep the interest in Burroughs alive. Over the years, each artist has brought a new dimension to the Burroughs novels. Each effort was important to the Burroughs mythos and helped maintain popularity at the time. I tried to do that for the nineties, with the express intent of honoring and following his characters.

I know Danton Burroughs really likes what I have done. It means a lot to me that the people who are closest to Burroughs' body of work appreciate my own work. I, in turn, have become really attached to the worlds of Burroughs. I can see myself returning to them over and over during the years. There is so much that I wanted to do with the characters and settings that I haven't been able to do yet. Eventually, I would like to return to the Mars theme. In fact, there are many other scenes I would like to have done and hope to do in the future. If I give myself some space, maybe another few years, I can add something new to the property. I need to get a new perspective, while letting this project settle in for awhile. Then, I'd like to go back and try to add something new.

Tarzan

THE DUM-DUM

Huge, fierce brutes stopped in their hunting, with up-pricked ears and raised heads, to listen to the dull booming that betokened the Dum-Dum of the apes... Tarzan was one of the wild, leaping horde. His brown, sweat-streaked, muscular body, glistening in the moonlight, shone supple and graceful among the uncouth, awkward, hairy brutes about him.

THE APE-MAN

A personification, was Tarzan of the Apes, of the primitive man, the hunter, the warrior. With the noble poise of his handsome head upon those broad shoulders, and the fire of life and intelligence in those fine, clear eyes, he might readily have typified some demigod of a wild and warlike bygone people of his ancient forest.

BOLGANI ATTACK

He had taken scarce a dozen steps toward the jungle when a great form rose up before him from the shadows of a low bush. At first he thought it was one of his own people but in another instant he realized that it was Bolgani, the huge gorilla.

So close was he that there was no chance for flight and little Tarzan knew that he must stand and fight for his life; for these great beasts were the deadly enemies of his tribe, and neither one nor the other ever asked or gave quarter... And since reason showed him that successful flight was impossible he met the gorilla squarely and bravely without a tremor of a single muscle, or any sign of panic.

TARZAN OF THE APES

LORD OF THE JUNGLE

    The man before him was the embodiment of physical perfection and giant strength; yet it was not upon these he depended in his battle with the great cat, for mighty as were his muscles, they were as nothing by comparison with Numa's. To his agility, to his brain and to his long keen knife he owed his supremacy.

ROGUE

He still grasped his spear, and while Tantor was yet six or eight paces behind his prey, a sinewy white warrior dropped as from the heavens, almost directly in his path. With a vicious lunge the elephant swerved to the right to dispose of this temerarious foeman who dared intervene between himself and his intended victim…

LA OF OPAR

Then the priestess, standing above him, began reciting what Tarzan took to be an invocation, the while she slowly raised her thin, sharp knife aloft. It seemed ages to the ape-man before her arm ceased its upward progress and the knife halted high above his unprotected breast.

STRANDED

The heat of the sun awoke him early in the forenoon. His first conscious sensation was of thirst, which grew almost to the proportions of suffering with full returning consciousness; but a moment later it was forgotten in the joy of two almost simultaneous discoveries.

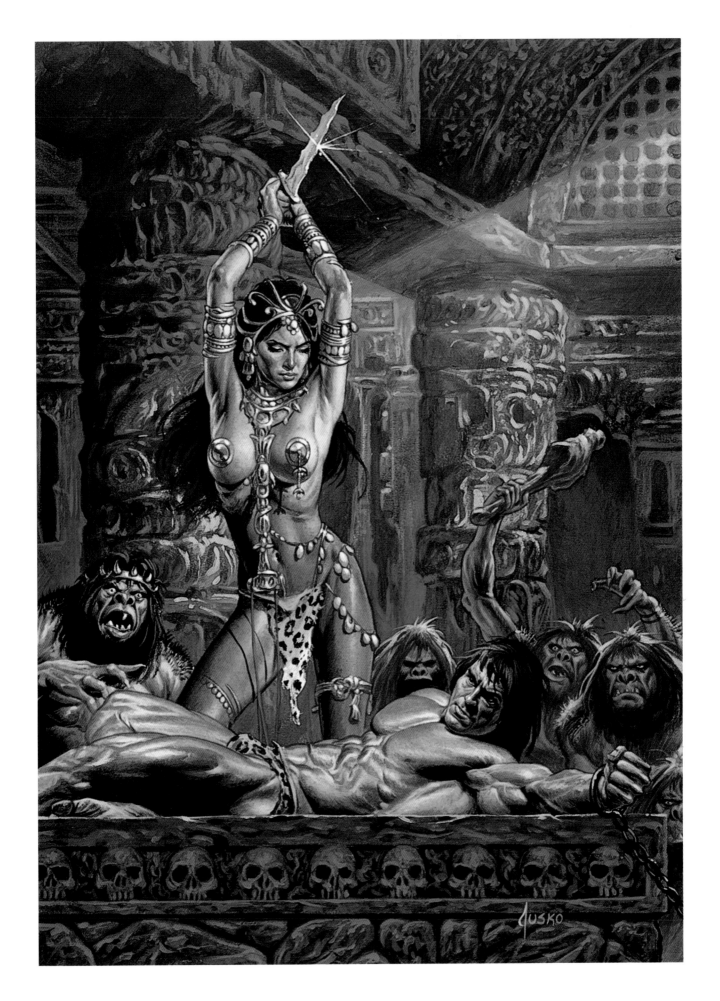

MOONLIGHT

The balance of the night the apes sat huddled close to one another for warmth… Tarzan and Sheeta, however, were of a different mind, for neither of them feared the jungle night, and the insistent craving of their hunger sent them off into the Stygian blackness of the forest in search of prey.

THE SACRIFICE

Tarzan of the Apes, tensing his mighty muscles, strained at the bonds that pinioned him; but they had been re-enforced many times at the instigation of the Russian, so that not even the ape-man's giant brawn could budge them… The dancers were leaping more closely to him now. The spears were commencing to find his body in the first torturing pricks that prefaced the more serious thrusts. It would not be long now. The ape-man longed for the last savage lunge that would end his misery.

SENTINEL

When he opened his eyes once more he found, much to his surprise, that he was not dead. He lay, securely bound, in the bottom of his own canoe. A great panther sat upon its haunches, looking down upon him. Kaviri shuddered and closed his eyes again, waiting for the ferocious creature to spring upon him and put him out of his misery of terror.

HUNTING PARTY

…for days the man, the panther, and the great apes roamed their savage haunts side by side, making their kills together and sharing them with one another, and of all the fierce and savage band none was more terrible than the smooth-skinned, powerful beast that had been but a few short months before a familiar figure in many a London drawing room.

JAWS OF DEATH

When Tarzan of the Apes realized that he was in the grip of the great jaws of a crocodile he did not, as an ordinary man might have done, give up all hope and resign himself to his fate. Instead, he filled his lungs with air before the huge reptile dragged him beneath the surface, and then, with all the might of his great muscles, fought bitterly for freedom. But out of his native element the ape-man was too greatly handicapped to do more than excite the monster to greater speed as it dragged its prey swiftly through the water.

DEATH THROES

And with flashing eyes and heaving bosom the girl, coming to her feet, ran to Korak's side to encourage him. Nearby lay The Killer's spear, where he had flung it as he charged the ape. The girl saw it and snatched it up. No faintness overcame her in the face of this battle primeval at her feet. For her there was no hysterical reaction from the nerve strain of her own personal encounter with the bull. She was excited; but cool and entirely unafraid.

AIRBORNE

With a bound he grasped a low limb, and with the agility of a little monkey swung himself and the boy to temporary safety. Nor did he hesitate even here; but raced on through the jungle night, bearing his burden to safety. For a time the bulls pursued; but presently, as the swifter outdistanced the slower and found themselves separated from their fellows they abandoned the chase, standing roaring and screaming until the jungle reverberated to their hideous noises.

MIDNIGHT RESCUE

Tantor broke through the palisade and charged the group. In the face of the maddened beast the crowd turned and fled, carrying Baynes backward with them. In a moment it was all over, and the elephant had disappeared with his prize; but pandemonium reigned throughout the village. Men, women and children ran helter skelter for safety. Curs fled, yelping. The horses and camels and donkeys, terrorized by the trumpeting of the pachyderm, kicked and pulled at their tethers....

THE HOSTAGE

And at last, when the raiders assembled after glutting their fury and their avarice, and rode away with her toward the north, she saw the smoke and the flames rising far into the heavens until the winding of the trail into the thick forests hid the sad view from her eyes.

TARZAN DOES NOT DESIRE YOU

"I cannot love you, La," said Tarzan in a low voice. "I do not know why, for you are very beautiful. I could not go back and live in Opar—I who have the whole broad jungle for my range…"

BACK, NUMA!

Not as an ordinary mortal might strike a blow did Tarzan of the Apes strike; but with the maddened frenzy of a wild beast backed by the steel thews which his wild, arboreal boyhood had bequeathed him.

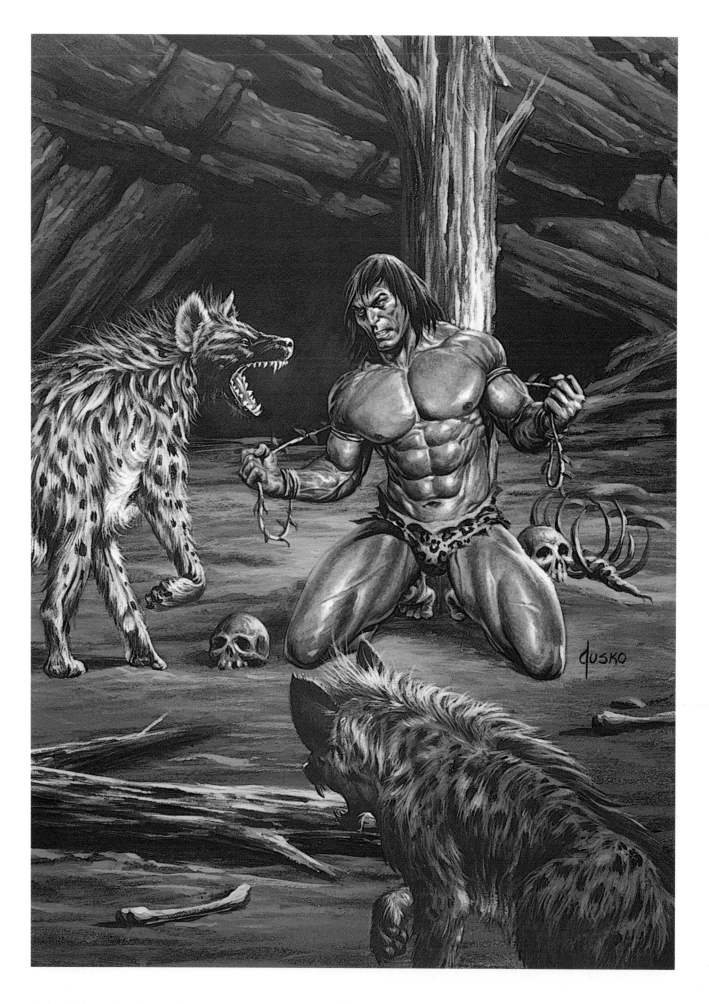

THE END OF BUKAWAI

The hyenas were sneaking furtively around the ape-man. Tarzan strained at his bonds for a moment, but soon realized that the rope he had braided to hold Numa, the lion, would hold him quite as successfully. He did not wish to die; but he could look death in the face now as he had many times before without a quaver.

THE NIGHTMARE

Nearer and nearer came the lion. Another moment and he could reach up with one great paw and drag the ape-man downward to those awful jaws. A whirring noise above his head caused Tarzan to glance apprehensively upward. A great bird was circling close above him...

TARZAN RESCUES THE MOON

...the ape-man fitted an arrow to his bow, and drawing the shaft far back, aimed its point at the heart of Numa where he lay in the heavens devouring Goro. There was a loud twang as the released bolt shot into the dark heavens. Again and again did Tarzan of the Apes launch his arrows at Numa, and all the while the apes of the tribe of Kerchak huddled together in terror.

TERRITORIAL DEFENSE

In the man's hand was the hunting knife of his long-dead father – the weapon that had first given him his real ascendency over the beasts of the jungle; but he hoped not to be forced to use it, knowing as he did that more jungle battles were settled by hideous growling than by actual combat, the law of bluff holding quite as good in the jungle as elsewhere—only in matters of love and food did the great beasts ordinarily close with fangs and talons.

BERTHA KIRCHER'S PERIL

No one can prophesy what a lion will do in any given emergency. This one glared and growled at the girl for a moment and then fell to feeding upon the dead horse. Fräulein Kircher wondered for an instant and then attempted to draw her leg cautiously from beneath the body of her mount; but she could not budge it...

SILENT AVENGER

There was no sound and it is doubtful that the German ever knew what manner of creature it was that alighted heavily upon his back, for at the instant of impact the sinewy fingers of the ape-man circled the hairy throat of the Boche.

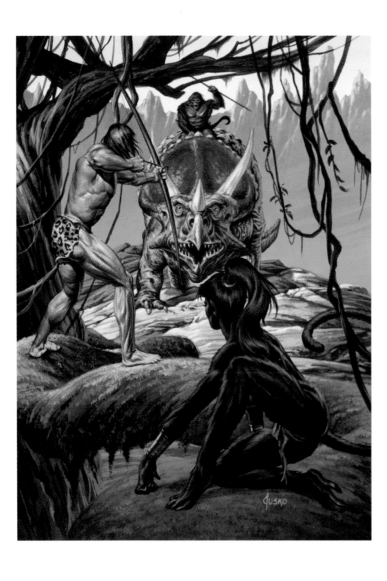

THE GRYF

And now the ridden *gryf* halted and looked up at them, bellowing… The Tor-o-don beat upon his breast and growled horribly—hideous, uncouth, beastly. Tarzan rose to his full height upon a swaying branch—straight and beautiful as a demigod—unspoiled by the taint of civilization—a perfect specimen of what the human race might have been had the laws of man not interfered with the laws of nature.

NARROW ESCAPE

Hidden amidst the plant life from the sight of any who might chance to pass along the well-beaten trail that skirted the river Pan-at-lee sought rest and food… there broke upon her ears from up the gorge the voices of shouting men—a sound that she recognized all too well. It was the war cry of the Kor-ul-lul. Closer and closer it approached her hiding place…

DEATH CLIMB

Tarzan raised the body of the dead Waz-don above his head, held it poised there for a moment as with face raised to the heavens he screamed forth the horrid challenge of the bull apes of the tribe of Kerchak, and with all the strength of his giant sinews he hurled the corpse heavily upon the ascending warrior…

SPECTRE

He heard her words; soft words of love
and endearment, and at the sound of the
voice and the scent spoor that a vagrant wind
carried suddenly to his nostrils, a strange
complex of emotion overwhelmed him—
happiness, despair, rage, love, and hate.

...and then Tarzan separated the grasses
and stepped to the very edge of the
embankment, his voice shattering the jungle
with a single word.

"Jane!" he cried...

ON THE VELDT

Hunting together, feeding together,
and sleeping together, the man and the
great lion trod the savage jungle trails
toward home. Yesterday they had shared
the meat of Bara, the deer, today they
feasted upon the carcass of Horta, the boar,
and between them there was little chance
that either would go hungry.

TWO-PRONGED ATTACK

"Quick! To your left!" he cried, and Tarzan, turning, saw two huge, green-eyed beasts crouching to spring. His first impulse was to rub his eyes as one might to erase the phantom figures of a disquieting dream, for what he saw were two ordinary African wildcats—ordinary in contour and markings, but in size gigantic.

LIMESTONE MONOLITH

For two days Tarzan followed a spoor that no other human eye might have discerned. On the afternoon of the second day he came upon a great stone cross built directly in the center of the ancient trail.

STAKED OUT

What was that? Blake strained his eyes into the darkness of the shadowy wood. Something was moving! Yes, it was the sound of stealthy, padded feet—the scraping of a furred body against leaves and twigs. The leopard of the wood was coming!

ARENA

The crowd roared in approbation. It enjoyed glorious sallies such as these. "I shall tear you limb from limb," shouted the murderer, and again the crowd applauded.

"I am here," said Tarzan, calmly.

"Flee!" screamed the murderer, and lowering his head he charged like an angry bull.

LANDSLIDE

At the turn where the footing was narrowest a stone gave beneath Tarzan's foot, throwing him off his balance for an instant and at that same instant Nkima, thinking that Tarzan was falling, shrieked and leaped from his shoulder, giving the ape-man's body just the impetus that was required to overbalance it entirely.

HATCHLINGS

The reptile was descending slowly toward its nest. The hideous demons below were screeching and hissing in anticipation. Tarzan's feet were almost in their jaws when he struck suddenly upward with his blade at the breast of the thipdar.

VANTAGE POINT

As she watched she saw another thipdar, much smaller, soaring above it. Suddenly the lesser one swooped upon its intended prey. Faintly she heard sounds of shattering and tearing and then the two combatants plunged earthward. As they did so she saw something separate itself from the mass and as the two creatures, partially supported by the wings of the larger, fell in a great, gliding spiral a most remarkable thing happened to the piece that had broken loose…

CAVE BEAR

The bear reared up and shook itself in an effort to dislodge the man-thing from its back, while Tarzan slipped a bronzed arm around the shaggy neck and clung desperately to his hold while he dragged his hunting knife from its sheath. It was a precarious place in which to stage a struggle for life. On one side the cliff rose far above them, and upon the other it dropped away dizzily into the depth of a gloomy gorge, and here the efforts of the cave bear to dislodge its antagonist momentarily bade fair to plunge them both into eternity.

TAWNY DEATH

…the lion charged, with the result that the beast, either carried forward by his own momentum or sensing escape, sprang into the corridor full in the faces of the advancing priests…

STAND OFF

The metal discs, elaborately wrought by the hands of some long-dead goldsmith of ancient Opar, rose and fell above her firm breasts as her heart beat, perhaps a bit more rapidly, beneath them. On came the leopard. She knew that in an instant he would charge; and then of a sudden he rose to his feet, his back arched, his mouth grinning in a fearful snarl...

FATAL PLUNGE

Slashing rapidly, but yet, at the same time, in accordance with a practical plan, she severed strand after strand in a straight line, as the rock dragged her downward toward the bottom. Constantly through her mind ran a single admonition—"Keep cool! Keep cool!" Should she permit herself to give away to hysteria, even for an instant, she knew that she must be lost. The lake seemed bottomless, the strands innumerable, while the knife grew constantly duller, and her strength appeared to be rapidly ebbing.

BELTHAR DOES NOT LIKE YOU

...the beast sprang to his feet with a terrific roar and leaped at the ape-man. The chains stopped him and he dropped down, growling.

"Belthar does not like you," said Nemone who had remained unmoved when the beast sprang. She noticed, too, that Tarzan had not started nor given any other indication that he had heard the lion or seen him; and she was pleased.

"He but reflects the attitude of all Cathne," replied Tarzan.

"That is not true," contradicted Nemone…"*I* like you."

THE GRAND HUNT

"Why is he running ahead?" asked Tarzan. "He will frighten away the quarry."

Pindes laughed. "He is the quarry."

"You mean—" demanded Tarzan with a scowl.

"That this is a grand hunt," cried Xerstle, "where we hunt man, the grandest quarry."

The ape-man's eyes narrowed. "I see," he said; "you are cannibals; you eat the flesh of men."

Gemnon turned away to hide a smile.

GIMLA ATTACK

…Tarzan climbed over the high cantle of the Abyssinian saddle and unslung his spear in the rather futile hope of holding the reptile at bay until his mount could reach the safety of the opposite bank toward which he was now attempting to guide him.

BALZA, THE WILD GIRL

He realized that their only chance of escape might be through this strange, beautiful, little savage, and he could not afford to antagonize her.

"Stanley," she repeated, stumbling a little over the strange word. "My name is Balza."

Tarzan thought that it fitted her well, for in the language of the great apes it meant golden girl.

DEADLY JUNGLE

The noon-day stop for lunch passed and the column took up its snakelike way through the forest once more. The ring of axes against wood ahead was accompanied by song and laughter. Already the primitive minds of the porters had cast off the fears that had assailed them earlier in the day.

Suddenly, without warning, a dozen feathered missiles sped from the apparently deserted forest around them. Two natives fell. Major White, walking beside Orman, clutched at a feathered shaft protruding from his breast and fell at Orman's feet. The askaris and the Arabs fired blindly into the forest. The column came to a sudden halt.

"Again!" whispered Rhonda Terry.

TARZAN AND THE LION MAN

TARZAN VERSUS LORD BUCKINGHAM

Suddenly the gorilla charged, and still the man held his ground. Great hairy paws reached out to seize him; but he eluded them with quick, panther-like movements. Stooping, he sprang beneath a swinging arm; and before the beast could turn leaped upon its back. A bronzed arm encircled the squat neck of the hairy Buckingham.

FISTS OF FURY

What followed after the bronzed body of the white man closed with that of the great cat defied her astonished eyes to follow. There was a swift intermingling of spotted hide and bronzed skin, of arms and legs, of talons and teeth; and above all rose the hideous growls of two blood-mad beasts. To her horror she realized that not the cat alone was the author of them; the growls of the man were as savage as those of the beast.

BLOOD FRENZY

He struck the lion at the shoulder
diagonally from above just as he reared
upon his hind legs to seize his victim. The
impact of the ape-man's body toppled the
lion upon its side. With a frightful roar, it
regained its feet but not before the ape-man
had locked his powerful legs around the
small of its body and encircled its massive
throat with one great arm.

DEATH FROM ABOVE

Now the lion was creeping toward her, belly to ground, the end of his tail twitching nervously. Just for a yard or so he came thus; then he rose, but still crouching a little as he advanced. Suddenly, with a mighty roar, he charged; and at the same instant a man leaped from a tree above full upon his back.

JURASSIC BATTLE

The warrior facing the great reptile with his puny spear was stunned to momentary inaction when he saw an almost naked bronzed giant drop, apparently from the blue, onto the back of the monster he had been facing without hope. He saw the stranger's knife striking futilely at the armored back, as the man clung with one arm about the creature's neck. He could have escaped; but he did not, and as Tarzan found a vulnerable spot in the dinosaur's throat and drove his knife home again and again, he rushed in to the ape-man's aid.

ANCIENT EXPLORER

Tarzan paused to investigate, for to him in his world nothing is too trivial to pass by without question. He saw that the skeleton… had lain there for a long time, years probably; which was entirely possible in this hot, dry plain. He could not tell how the man had come to his death, but he guessed that it might have been from thirst.

BREAKOUT

Tarzan walked to the window and examined the bars and the casing in which they were set.

"Stupid," he said.

"What is stupid?" asked Lord.

"Whoever designed this. Look." He seized two of the bars close to the sill and surged backward with all his strength and all his weight. There was a rending of wood as the entire window frame was torn from its seat; then he laid the frame with all its bars upon the floor of the room.

FINAL THRUST

Growls of fury rumbled from the savage throat of the great cat as it threw itself about in agony and rage. And, to Corrie's horror, mingled with them were equally savage growls that rumbled from the throat of the man. Incredulous, the three Americans watched the brief battle between the two—two jungle beasts—powerless to strike a blow for the man because of the wild leapings and turnings of the stricken tiger.

THE FATE OF ALL THIEVES

The following morning they started down toward the plain in search of the trail to the low country. On the way, they passed the scattered bones of Crump and Minsky now picked almost clean by hyenas, jackals and vultures.

CAGED FURY

Her eyes were on her cage mate; she saw the muscles of his shoulders and his arms tense as he exerted all their tremendous power upon the bars of his cage. And then she saw those bars slowly spread and Tarzan of the Apes step through to freedom.

Mars

THE CAPTIVE PRINCESS

But the sight that froze me with apprehension was that of Dejah Thoris and Sola standing there before him, and the fiendish leer of him as he let his great protruding eyes gloat upon the lines of her beautiful figure... She stood there erect before him, her head high held, and even at the distance I was from them I could read the scorn and disgust upon her face as she let her haughty glance rest without sign of fear upon him. She was indeed the proud daughter of a thousand jeddaks, every inch of her dear, precious little body; so small, so frail beside the towering warriors around her, but in her majesty dwarfing them into insignificance; she was the mightiest figure among them and I verily believe that they felt it.

THE BATTLE WITH ZAD

We circled for some time without doing much damage on either side; the long, straight, needle-like swords flashing in the sunlight, and ringing out upon the stillness as they crashed together with each effective parry. Finally Zad, realizing that he was tiring more than I, evidently decided to close in and end the battle in a final blaze of glory for himself...

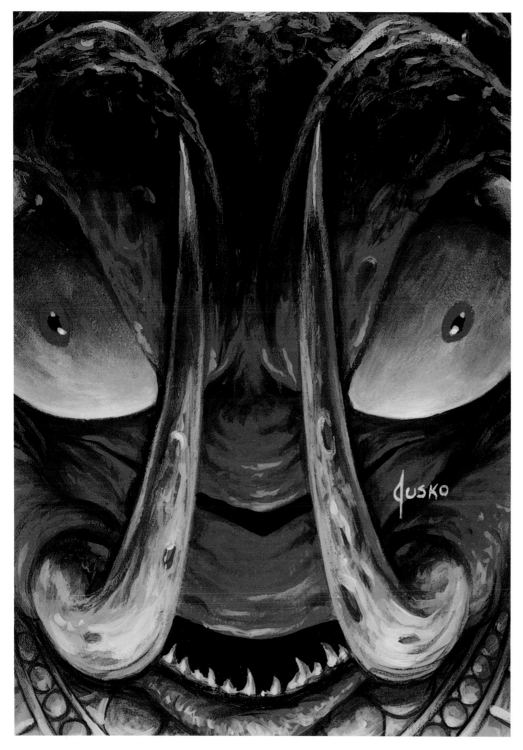

FACE OF DEATH

But I was to learn that the Martian smile is merely perfunctory, and that the Martian laugh is a thing to cause strong men to blanch in horror.

BABY THARK

Five or six had already hatched and the grotesque caricatures which sat blinking in the sunlight were enough to cause me to doubt my sanity.

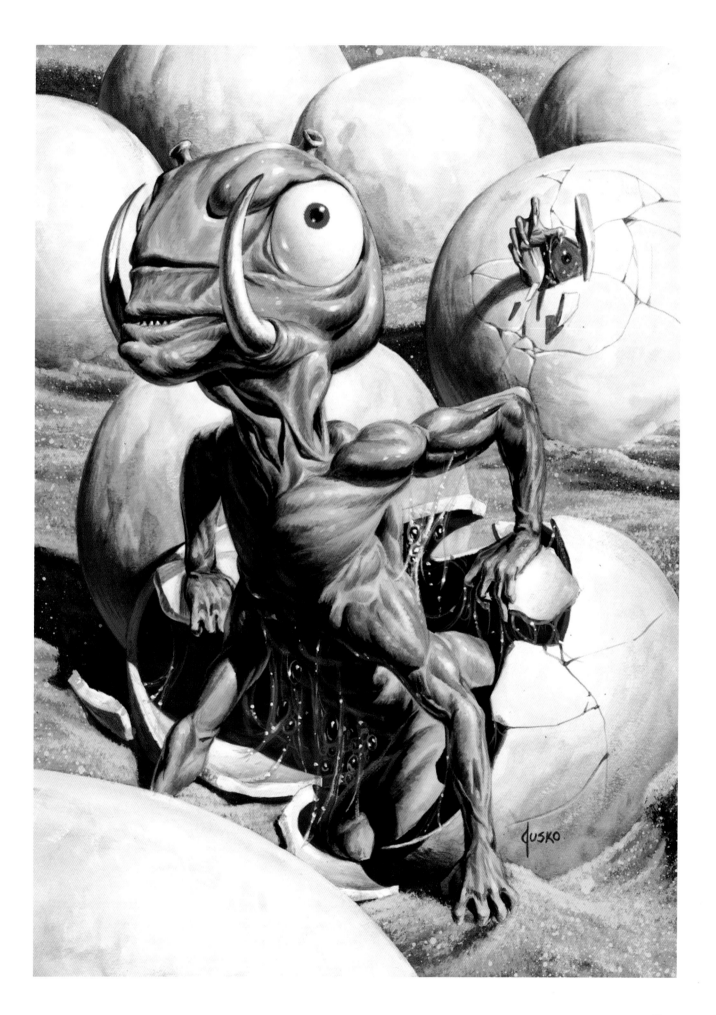

THE INDOMITABLE FOE

I must admit that he was a magnificent swordsman, and had it not been for my greater endurance and the remarkable agility the lesser gravitation of Mars lent me I might not have been able to put up the creditable fight I did against him.

MIDNIGHT RIDE

We rode all night and all the following day with only a few short rests. On the second night both we and our animals were completely fagged, and so we lay down upon the moss and slept for some five or six hours, taking up the journey once more before daylight.

ANCHOR IN THE AIR

The ship was floating slowly above us, not more than fifty feet over our heads. Instantly the one chance for escape that it offered presented itself to me. The vessel was slowly rising and now the anchor was beyond the blacks who faced me and several feet above their heads. With a bound that left them gaping in wide-eyed astonishment I sprang completely over them. A second leap carried me just high enough to grasp the now rapidly receding anchor.

EYES IN THE DARK

A faint shuffling sound behind me, and as I cast a hasty glance over my shoulder my blood froze in my veins for the thing I saw there. It was not so much fear of the present danger as it was the horrifying memories it recalled of that time I near went mad over the corpse of the man I had killed in the dungeons of the Warhoons, when blazing eyes came out of the dark recesses and dragged the thing that had been a man from my clutches and I heard it scraping over the stone of my prison as they bore it away to their terrible feast.

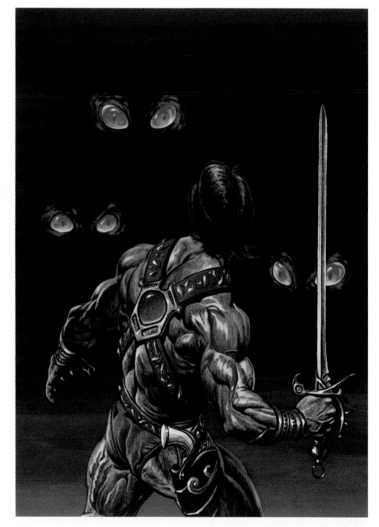

TARS TARKAS, CHAINED!

I hastened on as rapidly as I dared through the darkness until I reached the point at which they had left the corridor. There, through an open door, I saw them removing the chains that secured the great Thark, Tars Tarkas, to the wall.

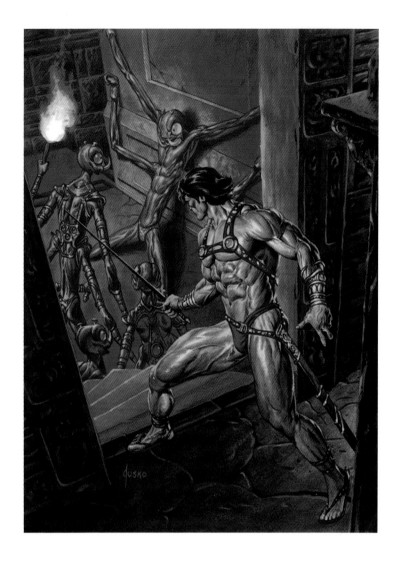

BACK TO BACK

Time and again the ferocious apes sprang in to close with us, and time and again we beat them back with our swords. The great tails of the plant men lashed with tremendous power about us as they charged from various directions or sprang with the agility of greyhounds above our heads; but every attack met a gleaming blade in sword hands that had been reputed for twenty years the best that Mars ever had known; for Tars Tarkas and John Carter were names that the fighting men of the world of warriors loved best to speak.

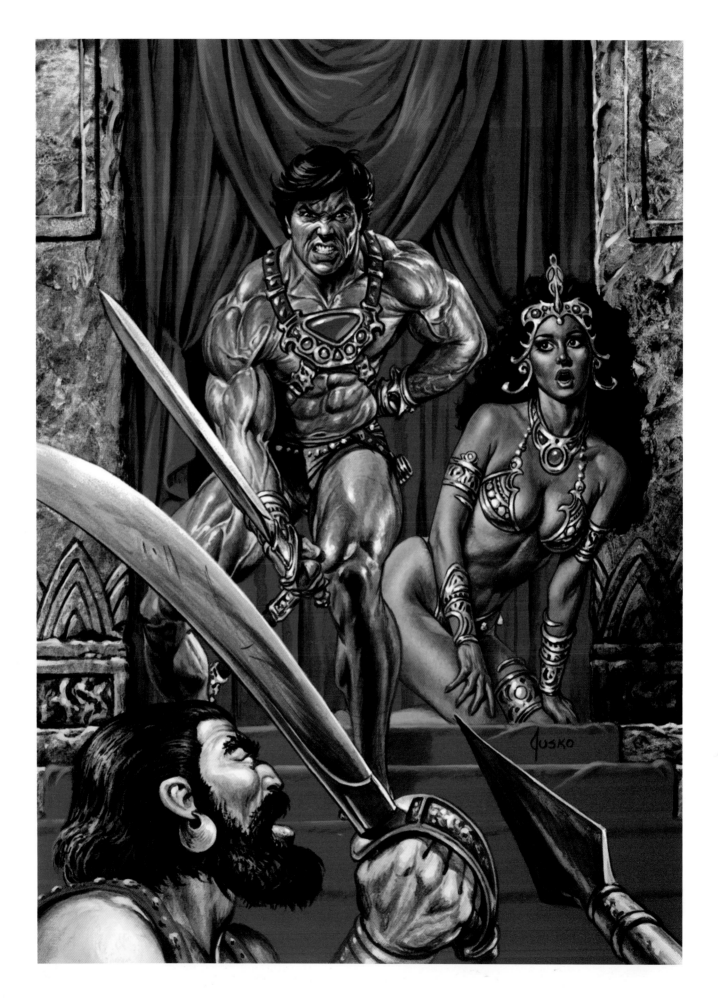

IN DEFENSE OF DEJAH THORIS

With a snarl he sprang toward me with naked sword, but whether Salensus Oll was a good swordsman or a poor I never learned; for with Dejah Thoris at my back I was no longer human—I was a superman, and no man could have withstood me then.

APT ENCOUNTER

For five days of cold and suffering and privation we traversed the rough and frozen way which lies at the foot of the ice-barrier. Fierce, fur-bearing creatures attacked us by daylight and by dark. Never for a moment were we safe from the sudden charge of some huge demon of the north.

CHAMBER OF REPTILES

To have attempted to cross that floor would have been to court instant death, and for a moment I was almost completely discouraged. Then it occurred to me that Thurid and Matai Shang with their party must have crossed it, and so there was a way.

MOUNTAIN STRONGHOLD

Here was the secret hiding place of Matai Shang, Father of Therns. Here, surrounded by a handful of the faithful, the hekkador of the ancient faith, who had once been served by millions of vassals and dependents, dispensed the spiritual word among the half dozen nations of Barsoom that still clung tenaciously to their false and discredited religion.

AFTERMATH

How long he lay there senseless he
could not guess; but when he opened his eyes
again he was alone, except for the bodies
of the dead green men and Dusarians, and
the carcass of a great banth that lay half
across his own.

THUVIA, MAID OF MARS

Her queenly head was poised haughtily upon her smooth red shoulders. Her dark eyes looked angrily into those of the man.

"You forget yourself, and the customs of Barsoom, Astok," she said. "I have given you no right thus to address the daughter of Thuvan Dihn, nor have you won such a right."

Thuvia, Maid of Mars
(detail)

THE HEADS THAT WALK

The impact hurled them both to the ground and as Tara of Helium sprang to her feet again she saw, to her horror, that the loathsome head had rolled from the body and was now crawling away from her on six short, spider-like legs. The body struggled spasmodically and lay still. As brief as had been the delay caused by the encounter, it still had been of sufficient duration to undo her, for even as she rose two more of the things fell upon her and instantly thereafter she was surrounded.

THE BATTLE OF THE KINGS

And then she saw and all those others saw a strange transition steal over the sword play of the Black Chief. It was as though he had been playing with the great dwar, U-Dor, all these hours, and now he still played with him but there was a difference. He played with him terribly as a carnivore plays with its victim in the instant before the kill.

BANTH ON BOARD

The banth slipped and clutched frantically at the deck. Gahan leaped in with his naked sword; the great beast caught itself and reared upon its hind legs to reach forth and seize this presumptuous mortal that dared question its right to the flesh it craved; and then the man sprang to the opposite side of the deck. The banth toppled sideways at the same instant that it attempted to spring; a raking talon passed close to Gahan's head at the moment that his sword lunged through the savage heart…

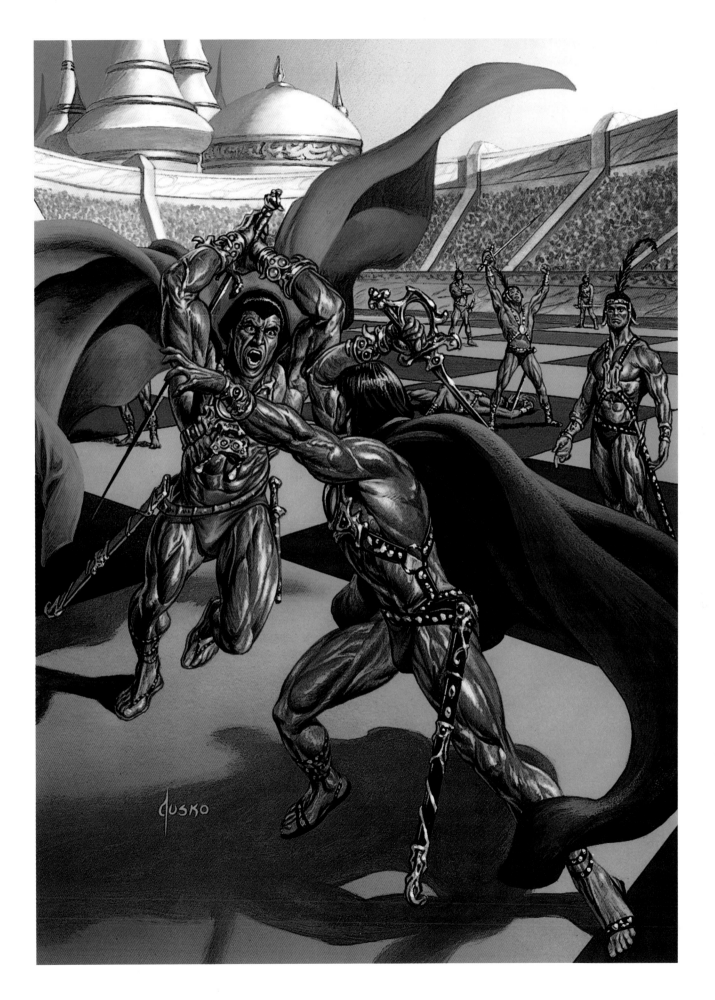

TREED BY BANTHS

Baffled, the banth gave vent to his rage and disappointment in a series of frightful roars that caused the very ground to tremble, and to these were added the roarings and the growlings and the moanings of his fellows as they approached from every direction, in the hope of wresting from him whatever of his kill they could take by craft or prowess.

STRANGLING THE ULSIO

It was such a thing that leaped upon the breast of the panthan to tear at his jugular. Twice Turan struck it away as he sought to regain his feet, but both times it returned with increased ferocity to renew the attack.

VENOMOUS ASSAULT

As it came towards me, apparently with the most sinister intentions, I hastily returned my dagger to its scabbard and drew my short sword, with which I struck at the fearsome-looking creature. As the blow descended, it drew back so that my point only slightly scratched it, whereupon it opened its hideous mouth and emitted a terrible scream so out of proportion to its size and to the nature of such insects with which I was familiar that it had a most appalling effect upon my nerves.

THE LABORATORY OF DESPAIR

Suffice it to say that at the end of four hours he had transferred the brain of each woman to the brain pan of the other, deftly connected the severed nerves and ganglia, replaced the skulls and scalps and bound both heads securely with his peculiar adhesive tape, which was not only antiseptic and healing but anaesthetic, locally, as well.

BARRICADE

As our eyes met, the creature voiced an angry growl and, abandoning its former stealthy approach, rushed swiftly up the ladder. Acting almost mechanically I did the one and only thing that might even temporarily stay its rush upon me—I slammed down the heavy trap-door above its head, and as I did so I saw for the first time that the door was equipped with a heavy wooden bar, and you may well believe that I lost no time in securing this, thus effectually barring the creature's ascent by this route into the veritable *cul de sac* in which I had placed myself.

THE WHITE DEATH

But whatever musing upon the flora of this strange land I may have been indulging in was brought to a sudden termination as we rounded the shoulder of a jutting promontory and came face to face with as hideous a creature as ever I had set my eyes upon. It was a great white lizard with gaping jaws large enough to engulf a man at a single swallow. At sight of us it emitted an angry hiss and advanced menacingly towards us.

AERIEL AMBUSH

He moved cautiously, looking around him at every step. He was still too close to the door. Very slowly he started across the cell, muttering to himself; and in the darkness above, I followed along the beam, like a panther stalking its prey. Still mumbling surprised exclamations, he started back. He passed beneath me; and as he did so, I sprang.

LAIR OF THE ASSASSIN

Slipping quietly over the eaves, I felt around with my toes until I found a projection that would support me. Then, releasing one hand, I felt for a new hold; and so, very slowly and carefully, I descended to the balcony.

ENCOUNTERING THE MASENA

I moved toward him, and again he changed his position. This time he placed himself in front of a blue panel, and I saw the yellow tint of his skin fade away and turn to blue… Here, indeed, was the most amazing of all the amazing creatures that I have ever seen.

I wondered if it were endowed with speech, and so I addressed it. "Kaor!" I said; "let's be friends," and I raised my sword hand above my head with the palm toward him, indicating my friendly intentions.

He looked at me for a moment; and then from his upper mouth issued strange sounds, like the purring and meowing of a cat.

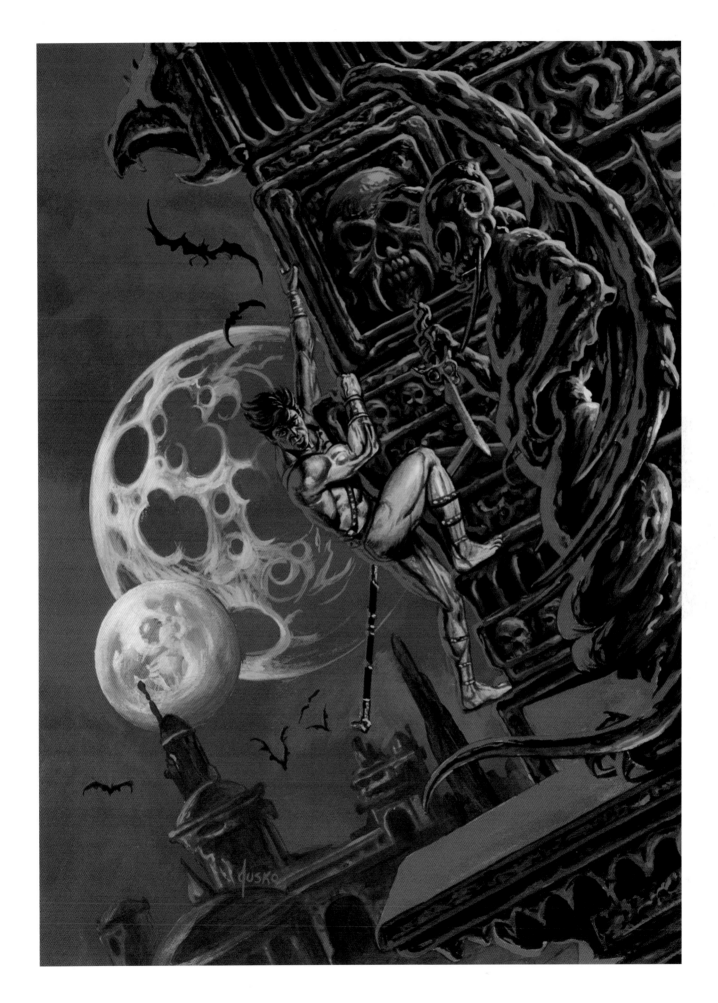

INVISIBLE MEN OF MARS

"You are most unco-operative," said the voice named Pnoxus. "I should hate to have to adopt unpleasant methods with you." The voice was not so sweet now; there was just a faint ring of steel in it.

"I don't know where you're hiding," I said; "but if you'll come out, all twenty of you, I'll give you a taste of steel. I have had enough of this foolishness."

"And I've had enough," snapped the voice. Somehow it sounded like a bear trap to me—all the oily sweetness had gone out of it. "Take him, men!"

BLACK PIRATES OF BARSOOM

The guard was coming closer when Llana darted to the door and pushed a heavy bolt into place; and not a moment too soon, for almost immediately I heard pounding on the door and the shouts of the warriors outside; and then I tripped upon a fur that had fallen from the couch during the struggle between Llana and Nastor, and I went down upon my back. Instantly Nastor leaped for me to run me through the heart. My sword was pointed up toward him, but he had all the advantage. I was about to die.

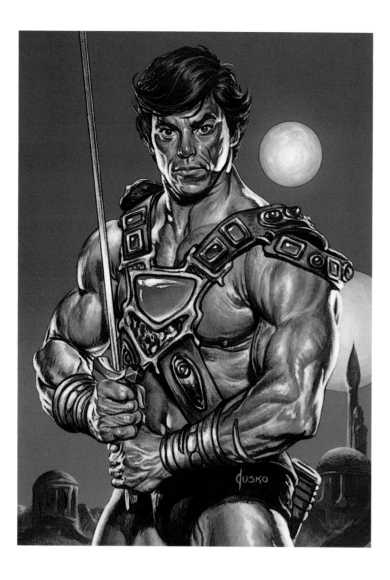

THE PRINCE OF HELIUM

Carter jerked his long sword from its scabbard and motioned Dejah Thoris to stay at his back. The silence of the forest was abruptly shattered by an uncanny roar directly above them.

THE HAND OF JOOG

The earthman had just seized his sword when he felt a rush of air above his head. There was a blur of motion as something came down toward him.

Now he felt himself clutched about the waist; then he was jerked fifty feet into the air. Struggling for breath, Carter clutched at the thing encircling his body.

THE JUPITER TREE

…the limbs of the trees moved like living things. They writhed and twined— myriad, snakelike things. I had scarcely noticed them until we halted. Suddenly one dropped down and wrapped itself about me. Smiling, I sought to disentwine it. I stopped smiling: I was as helpless as a babe encircled by the trunk of an elephant.

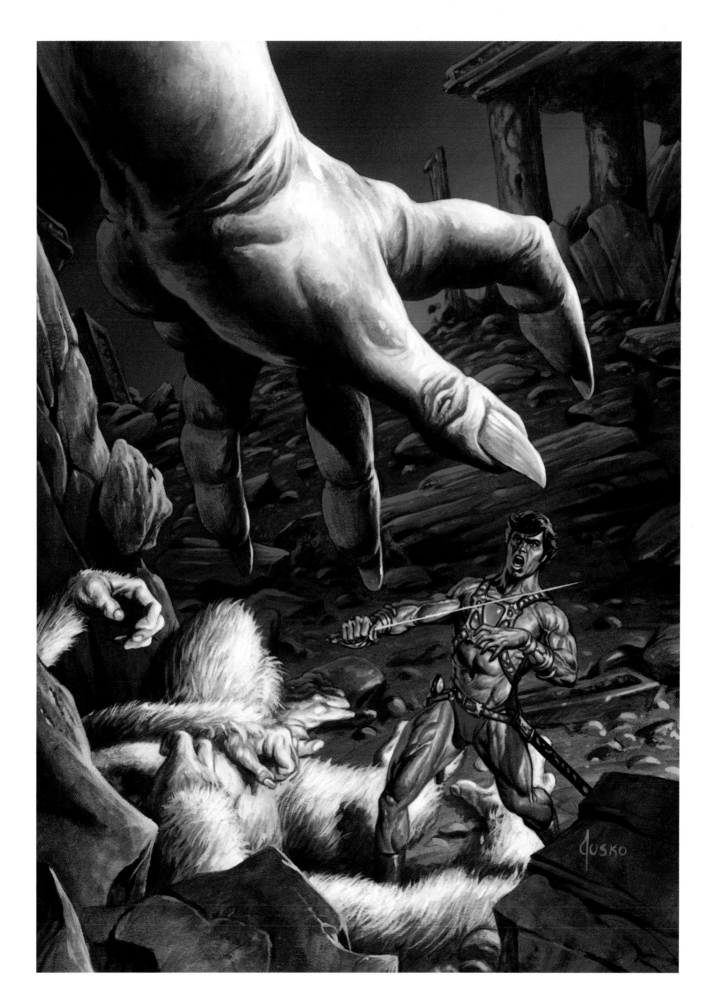

The Inner Worlds

page 95:

THIPDAR ATTACK

The hissing noise which had first attracted my attention was issuing from its throat, and seemed to be directed at something beyond and below me which I could not see. The ledge upon which I stood terminated abruptly a few paces farther on, and as I reached the end I saw the cause of the reptile's agitation.

MAHAR RITUAL

To the water's edge she came, nor did she even pause, but stepped into the shallows beside the little island. On she moved toward the Mahar, who now slowly retreated as though leading her victim on. The water rose to the girl's knees, and still she advanced, chained by that clammy eye. Now the water was at her waist; now her armpits. Her fellows upon the island looked on in horror, helpless to avert her doom in which they saw a forecast of their own.

NEANDERTHAL PURSUIT

I grasped my six-shooter by the barrel and hurled it squarely in his face with all my strength. Then, without waiting to learn the effect of my throw, I wheeled, ran the few steps to the edge, and leaped as far out over that frightful chasm as I could. I know something of diving, and all that I know I put into that dive, which I was positive would be my last.

OUTNUMBERED

...and as I glance toward them I saw three mighty *thipdars*—the winged dragons that guard the queen, or, as Perry calls them, pterodactyls—rise swiftly from their rocks and dart lightning-like, toward the center of the arena. They are huge, powerful reptiles. One of them, with the advantage which his wings might give him, would easily be a match for a cave bear or a tarag. These three, to my consternation, swooped down upon the tarag as he was gathering himself for a final charge upon me.

DROWNING THE TARAG

Choking, struggling, the maddened animal sought to reach the soft flesh of the man with his raking talons, but in the liquid element that filled the sea its usual methods of offense and defense were worthless. Quickly realizing that death stared it in the face, unless it could immediately overcome this handicap, the tarag now strained its every muscle to reach the solid footing of the land, while Tanar on his part sought to prevent it.

WOOLY MAMMOTH

The man shrugged resignedly. What a sentimental fool he had been! He might have known that this savage beast could not feel gratitude. He should have left it alone or put it out of its misery… Now it was too late. Presently it would overtake him and toss him. Such were his thoughts as he walked slowly along the trail. Overtake him it did. The sinuous trunk wrapped suddenly about him and he was lifted from the ground. "This," thought von Horst, "is the end."

IMPALED

The instant that it struck the ground in front of the men it leaped for von Horst. Skruf turned and fled, knocking Dangar down in his precipitate retreat. Von Horst had not even time to draw his pistol, so quickly was the thing upon him.

STRANGE FRIENDSHIP

Their presence with us more than repaid us for our efforts in behalf of the calf, for while they were with us we were never once menaced by any of the many predatory animals which abound in the country through which we passed, as even the most savage of them respect the strength of Maj.

TENTACLED TERROR

The canoe slipped through the water like a living thing, and U-Val was so pleased that he was almost decent. Several times—yes, many times—we were attacked by the fierce denizens of this paleolithic sea; but I had recovered my bow-and-arrows from beneath the cargo covering; and my arrows, together with U-Val's spears, always succeeded in averting the sudden death with which the terrible jaws of these horrific monsters threatened us.

ANTS

Again there was a conference of antennae, after which one of the ants led the two soldiers over toward us. It went directly to U-Val and touched him with its antennae.

"It is I," said U-Val.

"If they start to take you away, use your knife; and I will help you," I said.

The ant that had brought the soldiers over to us went away about its business; and then one of the soldiers advanced upon U-Val with opened mandibles.

"Now!" I called to U-Val, as I drew my stone knife.

SAVAGE PELLUCIDAR

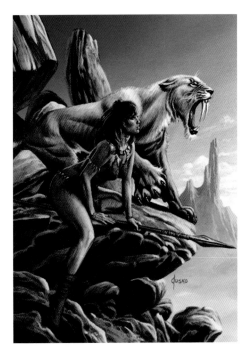

TIGER GIRL

Dian was awakened by something rubbing against her shoulder and opened her eyes to see one of the tarags nuzzling her. The other two had slumped down near her, but when she awoke they stood up…

PREHISTORIC ENCOUNTER

O-aa did not scream as the great jaws of the reptile opened wide to seize her, nor did she faint. Had our foremothers of the Stone Age wasted time screaming and fainting, when danger threatened, the human race would have died a-borning. And perhaps the world would have been a better, kinder place to live for all the other animals who do not constantly make war upon one another as do men. Like a human fly, O-aa scrambled up the face of the cliff a few feet; then she looked back and made a face at Tylosaurus, after which she considered carefully her new position.

DIAN THE BEAUTIFUL

"They will not hurt us," said Dian. "They are my friends. Every time that I can, I bring them pieces of meat."

╪Venus╪

ATTACK OF THE TARGA

"Be ready," cautioned Kamlot; "he will charge."

The words had scarcely crossed the lips of the Vepajan when the hideous creature rushed toward us. Its body and legs were covered with long, black hair, and there was a yellow spot the size of a saucer above each eye. It screamed horribly as it came, as though to paralyze us with terror.

page 109:

THE KLANGAN

Hovering just above us, I saw what at first appeared to be five enormous birds; but which I soon recognized, despite my incredulity, as winged men. They were armed with swords and daggers, and each carried a long rope at the end of which dangled a wire noose.

"Voo klangan!" shouted Kamlot. (The bird-men!)

Even as he spoke a couple of wire nooses settled around each of us. We struggled to free ourselves, striking at the snares with our swords, but our blades made no impression upon the wires, and the ropes to which they were attached were beyond our reach.

THE KLOONOBARGAN

As we turned to retrace our steps a chorus of hoarse shouts arose upon all sides of us—half human, half bestial, like the growls and roars of animals blending with the voices of men; and then, suddenly, from behind the boles of trees a score of hairy, manlike creatures sprang toward us.

THARBAN

A screaming, clawing hellion of unrestrained primitive rage and hate, the great carnivore hurtled upward within a few feet of Duare and me; and then, still clawing and screaming, it fell back. Like a huge cat, that it most closely resembled, it came down feet first. With ready horns and tail stiffly erect, the basto waited to catch it and toss it again.

LULA'S PLIGHT

As the beast charged, the man turned to face it with his pitifully inadequate spear, for he must have known that flight was futile. I had drawn my Amtorian pistol, charged with its deadly r-ray; and as I flattened out just above the tharban, narrowly missing a crack-up, I let him have it.

ESCAPE ON VENUS

THE MYPOSAN

"I had no more than reached it than some one seized me around the waist, leaped to the rail with me, and then into the lake. It was a Myposan! You know how these fellows swim, my prince. Half the time he had me under water, half drowned; but at last he dragged me ashore at Mypos, more dead than alive."

THE AMOEBA MEN

The creature's struggles were now become violent; its groans and screams filled the vast chamber, echoing and re-echoing from the domed ceiling; and then, to my horror, I saw that the creature was splitting apart along the reddish median line I have described—right down the center of its head and body.

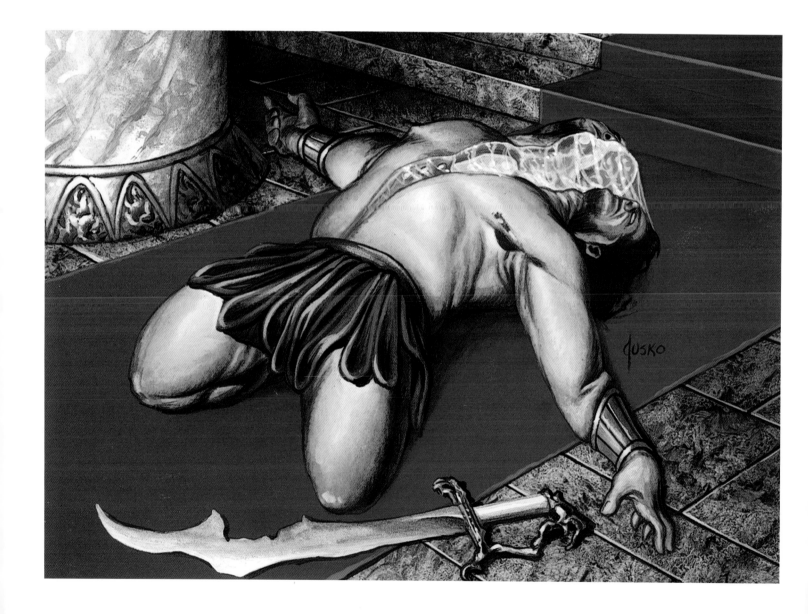

THE BOILING SEA

Already the effects of the catastrophe were becoming plainly discernible below us. The fleeter reptiles and fishes were fleeing the holocaust—and they were fleeing north! Instinct or intelligence, or whatever it was, it filled me with renewed hope.

Sea Beasts

We often flew low to observe the strange and savage marine life which occasionally broke the surface of the sea—huge monsters of the deep, some of which attained the dimensions of an ocean liner. We saw millions of lesser creatures fleeing before fearsome carnivorous enemies. We saw titanic battles between monstrous leviathans— the age-old struggle for survival which must exist upon every planet of the Universe upon which life exists…

SPELLCASTER

We were conducted to the foot of the steps leading up to the dais. The man, whom I assumed to be Morgas, looked us over carefully… The room was very quiet, there was not a sound, when suddenly he shouted, "Silence! I cannot endure this infernal noise. Chop off their heads! Chop off their heads! Then, perhaps, I shall have peace."

Miscellaneous Stories

THE PEOPLE THAT TIME FORGOT

THE STALKING WEIROO

"I waited, scarce breathing, watching the thing creep stealthily toward me, its great eyes luminous in the darkness of the cave's interior, and at last I knew that those eyes were directed upon me, for the Wieroo can see in the darkness better than even the lion or the tiger."

OUT OF TIME'S ABYSS

page 119

TYRANNOSAUR

The creature saw Bradley almost at the same instant that he saw it and reared up on its enormous hind legs until its head towered a full twenty-five feet above the ground. From the cavernous jaws issued a hissing sound of a volume equal to the escaping steam from the safety-valves of half a dozen locomotives, and then the creature came for the man.

PLESIOSAUR

It turned its eyes upon us, opened its lizard-like mouth, emitted a shrill hiss and came for us. The thing must have been sixteen or eighteen feet in length and closely resembled pictures I had seen of restored plesiosaurs of the lower Jurassic. It charged us as savagely as a mad bull, and one would have thought it intended to destroy and devour the mighty U-boat, as I verily believe it did intend.

THE MUCKER

KNOCKOUT

...but Billy couldn't leave the booze alone, and so the best that he got was an occasional five spot for appearing in preliminary bouts with third- and fourth-rate heavies and hasbeens; but during the three years that he had hung about Hilmore's he had acquired an enviable knowledge of the manly art of self-defense.

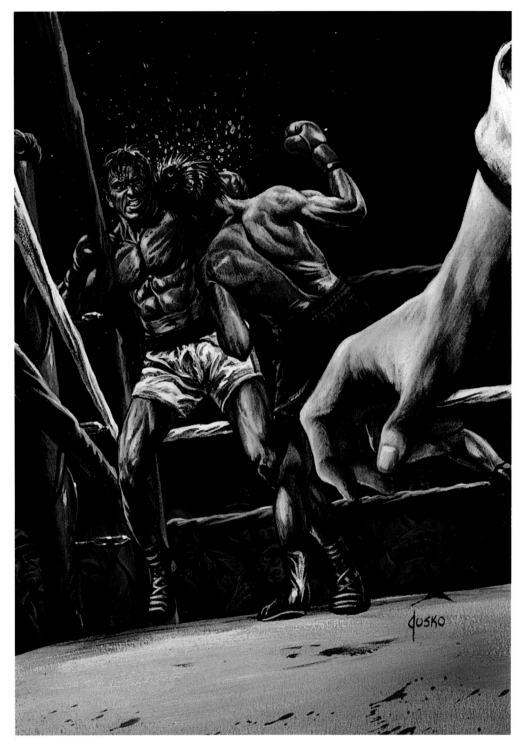

CANNIBAL FRENZY

"Your name?" he asked.

"Nah-ee-lah," she replied.

"Nah-ee-lah," he repeated, "Ah, you are the daughter of Sagroth, Jemadar of Laythe."

She nodded in indifferent affirmation, as thought aught he might say was a matter of perfect indifference to her.

"What do you expect us to do with you?" asked Ga-va-go, a question which suggested a cat playing with a mouse before destroying it.

"What can I expect of the Va-gas, other than that they will kill me and eat me?" she replied.

page 124:

KIDNAPPED

For a long distance he carried her, his little pig eyes searching and straining to right and left into the black night for the first sign of savage beast. The half-atrophied muscles of his little ears, still responding to an almost dead instinct, strove to prick those misshapen members forward that they might catch the first crackling of dead leaves beneath the padded paw of the fanged night prowlers. But the wood seemed dead. No living creature appeared to thwart the beast-man's evil intent. Far behind him Thandar slept. Thurg grinned.

page 125:

QUICK DRAW

I drew my pistol from its holster, but Bantor Han laid a hand upon my arm.

"Don't shoot it," he said, "you may make it angry. If we go away and leave this meat to it, it probably will not attack us."

"If you think I am going to leave our supper to that thing, you are very much mistaken," I said.

NEAR MISS

I stood there, resting, for a moment, preparatory to turning and retracing my steps to the launch, when, without warning, something whizzed through space straight toward me. There was a dull thud of impact as it struck the tree, and as I dodged to one side and turned to look at the thing I saw a heavy spear imbedded in the wood not three inches from where my head had been.

PAINTINGS